Grammar B

G000041878

Contents

unit 1

Revising and investigating verb tenses

 Key idea

Verbs change form to distinguish between their three main tenses or times.

> Yesterday I **felt** ill, today I **feel** sickly, but tomorrow I **will feel** better.

- The main tenses are past, present and future.
- Verbs may be regular and irregular in their formation of tenses.
- Past tenses may be particularly difficult.

Other words in the sentence must fit in with the verb's tense.

 Top Tip

The past tense is formed usually by adding **–ed** to the base verb. Awkward, irregular past forms are usually given in a dictionary.

Try it out! •

Identify the verbs in these sentences, and state their tenses. *(1 mark for each correct answer)*

1 Last year, many things went wrong at Wizardry College.
2 In particular, they had one very strange professor.
3 He did a great deal of harm to the school.
4 He ruined the school's reputation for magic.
5 As a result, Wizardry College lies bottom of the league.
6 In addition, the Chief Magician is still off sick.
7 However, he will return next week.
8 Fortunately, there is no sign of odd Professor Doodle now.
9 Surprisingly, people still feel nervous.
10 What else will go wrong?

Keep practising!

Use a dictionary to help you fill in the other verb tenses. The first one has been done to help you. *(0.5 mark for each correct answer)*

simple present	simple past	simple future
I throw	*I threw*	*I will throw*
I have		
I am		
I find		
I wake		
I sing		
I bring		
I grow		
I go		
I catch		
I teach		

Take up the challenge!

The writer meant to write this narrative in the past tense. Carelessly, he often slipped into the present tense. Find and correct the ten mistakes. *(1 mark for each correct answer)*

The Chief Magician returned to the Academy. At first, all went well; then the rumours start. One teacher thought he recognises a frightening figure floating down the path. Another magician is sure he sees a looming face in the car park. The Spellmaster thinks he glimpses a ghost at the back of assembly. The cook bumps into him in the dining hall. What was he doing there? How can he be back at Wizardry? Finally, the Spellmaster confronts him. Desperately, he tried to get rid of him before the Chief Magician comes out of his office. Too late! The bell rings.

Verb tenses

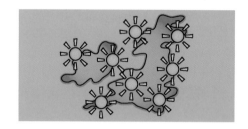

 Key idea

The choice of tense may be decided by the purpose of the text.
* Narratives are best written in the past tense.
  The story **began** long ago.
* Explanations are usually written in the present tense.
  Modern devices **save** time.
* Forecasts use the future tense.
  We **will have** rain tomorrow.

Try it out! ·

★ **Top Tip**
Be careful not to slip from past to present tense in your narratives.

Choose the correct label for each of these sentences. Either:
* narrative: past tense or
* explanation: present tense or
* forecast/prediction: future tense.

An example has been given to help you. *(1 mark for each correct answer)*

    Once upon a time, there was a boy called Solomon. (narrative)

1   The weather will be bright with some warm sunshine.
2   A successful classroom experiment requires the correct materials.
3   The temperature will reach 23° celsius in the shade.
4   Very high temperatures cause environmental problems.
5   During his absence, the mystery deepened.

6 Indoor plants need regular supplies of food and water.

7 The householders will spend the night in temporary accommodation.

8 Insulators are not electricity conductors.

9 The George Hotel will be the last building on the right.

10 After a flash of light, a tiny man appeared.

Keep practising! ·

Make up and label ten new sentences of your own. Try to write some of each type. *(1 mark for each sentence)*

Take up the challenge! ·

The author planned her story in note form. Use her notes to write the first paragraph of the story. Remember, this is a narrative so you need to use the past tense. *(10 marks)*

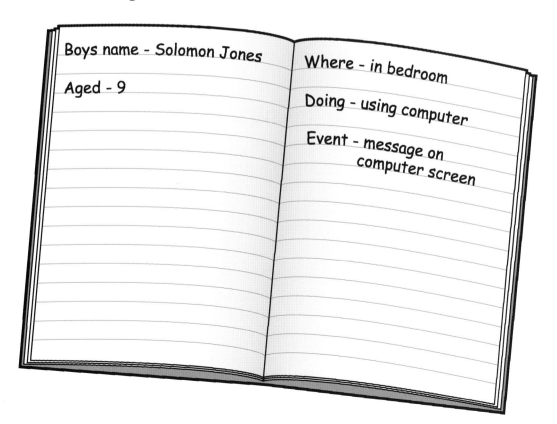

Boys name - Solomon Jones

Aged - 9

Where - in bedroom

Doing - using computer

Event - message on computer screen

unit 3 Identifying verbs

 Key idea

One way of testing whether or not a word is a verb is to try to change its tense.

> Year 4 **study** movement.
> Year 4 **studied** movement.

- By experimenting with changing tense, you can confirm that a word is a verb.
- If you are sure that a word is a verb, it can help you to improve sentence construction.

 Top Tip

Can the meaning of the word move to a different time? Use this test to help identify a verb.

Try it out! •

These sentences are from a science textbook. Change them from past to present tense then underline the word you changed in each. It should be a verb! *(1 mark for each correct answer)*

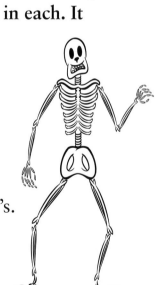

1 The human body had a skeleton of bones.
2 The bones of the body were joined.
3 Joints gave a great range of movement.
4 The skeleton grew from birth.
5 The rate of bone growth varied among people.
6 One 9-year-old's forearm was longer than another's.
7 The skeleton supported the body's organs.
8 The skeleton also protected the body's organs.
9 Bones and muscles helped with human movement.
10 Muscles also assisted the movement of the body.

Can you identify the verbs from the words below? Use the tense-change test to help you. *(1 mark for each correct answer)*

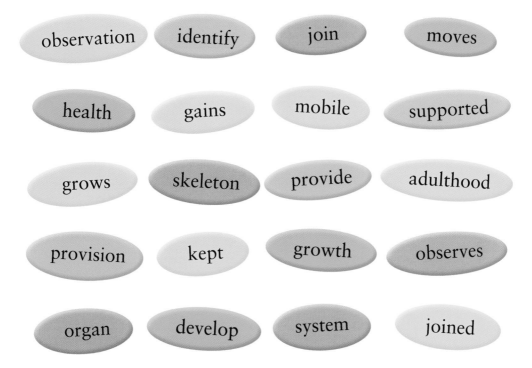

observation   identify   join   moves

health   gains   mobile   supported

grows   skeleton   provide   adulthood

provision   kept   growth   observes

organ   develop   system   joined

Take up the challenge! ●

This is a live radio netball commentary. Only ten of the highlighted words are verbs. Identify and change them to write a newspaper sports report in the past tense. *(1 mark for each correct answer)*

Joseph Tolyffe School **has** the **pass**. They **pass** from Wing to Centre to Goal Attack. The **Shooter, cool** and ready, **shoots** and ... no! The Broad Street Goalkeeper **does** a brilliant **interception**. He **gets** it out to Goal Defence, who **sends** it over the **head** of the tiny Goal **Attack**. Broad Street **seizes control**, from Centre to Goal Attack. Goal Shooter **receives** the ball, **tosses** it high **into** the **air** and ... yes! The **score stands** at Broad Street 1 Joseph Tolyffe 0.

Powerful verbs

 **Key idea**

A powerful verb gives extra meaning to a sentence. As well as telling us what is happening, it conveys atmosphere and mood.

The teacher **wrung** his hands and **mopped** his brow.

- A powerful verb acts as a descriptive word.
- One powerful verb can be more effective than a weak verb and an adverb.
- A powerful verb can remove the need for too many adjectives.

Try it out! •

Rewrite the sentences, replacing each underlined phrase with a powerful verb from the box below. Remember to change the powerful verb to the appropriate tense.

(1 mark for each correct answer)

 Top Tip
Think before you use a verb with an adverb or adjective. Would one very powerful verb give the same information?

mumble	wreck	understand	growl	spin
glower	return	terrify	stroll	abandon
	revisit	glare	trudge	ruin	bar
mutter	collapse	welcome	glimpse	ban

1 The clown <u>walked wearily</u> away from the tent.
2 He could not <u>get fully in his mind</u> what all the fuss was about.
3 "It's most odd," he <u>said quietly to himself</u>.

4   "Why have I been <u>looked at in an unfriendly way</u>?"

5   "All I wanted was to <u>go into</u> the ring <u>again</u>."

6   However, the other circus performers did not <u>have friendly feelings about</u> Pongo.

7   They wanted him to be <u>kept away completely</u> from the circus.

8   They did not want to <u>see</u> him, <u>even briefly</u>.

9   After all, he had <u>made</u> the circus's reputation <u>very bad</u>.

10 He had <u>made</u> the children <u>really frightened</u>.

Keep practising! •

Make up sentences for the ten unused verbs in the box of powerful verbs from Try it out! Avoid putting unnecessary words in your sentences. *(1 mark for each sentence)*

Take up the challenge! •

The writer needs to shorten this text. Using ten powerful verbs instead of the highlighted words will do the trick.

(1 mark for each correct answer)

The Ringmaster **used a loud voice**, as he **said** his words **again**. The words **went over and over** in the lion tamer's head, and she **hoped** for quiet. She **asked** the Ringmaster **in a begging voice** to stay calm, but he **laughed sarcastically** at her claims.

"Gone? Never!" he **said firmly**. "Pongo will **be back**."

The lion tamer **walked** up and down; she **looked very angry**.

unit 5

Identifying adverbs

 Key idea

Adverbs add to (qualify) the meaning of verbs, and give interest and detail to the sentence.

It is surprisingly hot today.

- Adverbs often, but not always, end with **–ly** suffix.
- They are often positioned just after the verb.
- Many adverbs answer the questions "How?" "When?" "Where?" and "How often?"

When?   Where?   How often?

Yesterday they checked outside regularly.

Try it out! ·

⭐ **Top Tip**
To identify the adverb, look for the word that adds to the verb.

Identify one adverb in each sentence.

(1 mark for each correct answer)

1 The tiger prowled ruthlessly through the jungle.
2 She had smelt food, and she wanted that prey desperately.
3 She watched, waited, and searched thoroughly, but found no victim.
4 In order to feed her cubs properly, she needed fresh meat.
5 Suddenly, she remembered the water hole.
6 She made her stealthy way there.
7 "I see them well!" she hissed.
8 "Obviously, they have forgotten my power."
9 The tiger had guessed correctly, and the giraffes were easy prey.
10 Then the mother had what she needed.

The words underlined are examples of adjectives or adverbs. Unfortunately, they have become jumbled. Draw two boxes, one headed "adverbs" and one headed "adjectives", and put ten phrases in each. *(0.5 mark for each correctly identified word)*

she felt <u>well</u>

wore a <u>woolly</u> jumper

arrived <u>early</u>

started <u>late</u>

a <u>loud</u> engine

was a <u>good</u> idea

a <u>silly</u> joke

a <u>careful</u> driver

he hid it <u>craftily</u>

it happened <u>then</u>

<u>lovely</u> weather

agreed <u>now</u>

in <u>neat</u> handwriting

he walked <u>fast</u>

left <u>promptly</u>

the <u>early</u> post

<u>finally</u> she admitted it

a <u>fast</u> journey

was <u>really</u> in a mess

had a <u>scheming</u> mind

Identify the ten adverbs here. Which verbs do they qualify?
(0.5 mark for each correct answer)

Reluctantly, the old lion was leaving. He had begged desperately to be allowed to stay King. He said that he really wanted to see his people again, and to talk briefly to some of them. The wolf – she was his one, real friend – agreed. Soon the visit was arranged, but on the strict condition that he moved fast. He was not to spend a long time in the undergrowth, or dawdle unnecessarily. On the actual day, he behaved carelessly, and things did not go well.

Collecting and classifying adverbs

 Key idea

Adverbs can be classified (grouped) according to what they mean. Collections of adverbs which belong to the same subject form useful word banks.

- Mother stared **nervously**.
- The gardener acted **timidly**.
- Cook was the one who acted **bravely**.

Try it out! ·

Which page does each adverb belong to? List five adverbs under each page heading. Choose from *Number, Speed, Mood* or *Light*.

(0.5 mark for each correct answer)

 Top Tip
If you are searching for an adverb with a similar meaning, think of using a thesaurus.

dimly	sparingly	briskly	numerously	hazily
sluggishly	happily	clearly	abundantly	pensively
swiftly	sparsely	nervously	sadly	dazzlingly
hastily	confidently	plentifully	quickly	faintly

·NUMBER· ·SPEED· ·MOOD· ·LIGHT·

Keep practising!

Identify the ten adverbs. *(1 mark for each correct answer)*

Cook moved acrobatically. She was able to glide silently through her kitchen and to dash nimbly from place to place. When the main door had been locked, she had climbed lithely through an open window. This creature, half animal and half human, could do the same – but he did not move athletically. He scraped loudly against the window frame and slithered clumsily through the gap. He lost his balance, fell awkwardly against the cupboard, flung out an arm jerkily, and made the crockery crash deafeningly to the floor.

Take up the challenge!

Think of four adverbs to link with each of these actions. For example,
spoke *harshly*
looked *quickly*
(0.5 mark for each correct answer)

1   the way you speak
2   the way you look at something
3   the way you eat
4   the way you dress
5   the way you buy presents

Changing adverbs

 Key idea

Using the right adverb can save words, as well as improving the style of a sentence.

> The small child told her story in a tearful manner.
> The small child told her story **tearfully**.

- An adverb may replace a phrase, as in the example above where "in a tearful manner" has been replaced with the adverb "tearfully".
- A word in the phrase can often be made into an adverb, for example, "tearful" has been changed into "tearfully".
- Choosing the best adverb is important.

Try it out! •

 **Top Tip**
Be ready to think carefully about your choice of adverb.

Replace the words underlined with an adverb. Be careful to retain the sentence's original meaning. *(1 mark for each correct answer)*

1 Zoe felt <u>in a strong way</u> that the farmer had problems.
2 He behaved <u>in a strange way</u>.
3 Everyone in the village treated him <u>in an unpleasant way</u>.
4 Local shopkeepers complained a <u>constant amount</u>.
5 Children looked at him <u>as if they were fearful</u>.
6 Other farmers avoided him <u>with lots of care</u>.
7 Letters of complaint arrived <u>every single day</u>.
8 He had often looked at Zoe <u>as if he was sad</u>.
9 She felt that he should be treated <u>in a respectful way</u>.
10 That was why she schemed <u>in a foolish way</u>.

Match the adverb to the phrase it could replace.

(1 mark for each correct answer)

phrases	adverbs
with no care	early
with a lot of sound	well
at steady intervals	loudly
in a good way	regularly
with no sound	reluctantly
bit by bit	gradually
in good time	carelessly
in the end	noiselessly
at the exact, right time	finally
as if not wanting to	promptly

A change of adverb can bring a change of meaning. Make this story a happy one by replacing the ten adverbs with different adverbs.

(1 mark for each correct answer)

The farmer worked unhappily and slowly at Brook Farm. His staff worked together nervously. They knew they grew crops badly. The vegetables were never tasty; other crops always failed. The local land inspector visited and spoke angrily to the farmer. The inspector talked critically of the condition of the fields. He said he would write unfavourably to the Local Authority. The farmer looked anxiously at the land inspector's face.

Using commas

unit 8

 **Key idea**

Commas within a sentence help the reader; they mark breaks in the sense.

> The weather, which was awful, spoilt their holiday.

• Commas separate the sentence into parts.
• The parts are meaningful units.
• The commas follow the pattern of spoken language.

The commas are used to mark additional information and lists of actions.

> Mr Khan, a man known for his kindness, offered to help.
> Don't forget to bring your pencil, ruler, rubber and paper.

Try it out! •

The writer has supplied extra details about his characters. Use a pair of commas to separate the additional information from the main sentence. *(1 mark for each sentence with correct use of commas)*

 Top Tip
Read sentences aloud. The rise and fall of your voice should match your commas.

1   Molly Flint the outstanding junior athlete had disappeared.
2   Miss Grimes the local librarian was mystified.
3   Josh Flint her younger brother did not care.
4   Sarah Flint Molly's organised mother did not like problems.
5   As for Jack Flint Molly's noisy father he disliked fuss.
6   Emma Crumble the young girl next door was sympathetic.
7   Mr Smallwood a man known for his calmness looked worried.

8   Bob Jordan the local fireman gave advice.

9   Mrs Smithers the school cook stopped baking cakes.

10 Local people only the ones without small children to look after joined in the search.

Keep practising!

Fit the additional information into the sentences. Remember to use pairs of commas. *(2 marks for each correct answer)*

1   Molly had gone into a daydream.
2   That television programme was to blame.
3   The hero's voice had wrecked the story.
4   A newsreader interrupted the story.
5   She had a message to convey.

additional information

a very urgent one
her face very serious
a dull and monotonous drone
the one with the boring plot
closing her eyes

Take up the challenge!

Ten commas have been left out. Some work in pairs, some on their own, but they all mark additional information. Reading aloud will help you place them. *(1 mark for each correct answer)*

At this moment Molly made her daydream as vivid as possible. It was a beach a sandy spot in the Caribbean with bright blue sky and sea. The girl her eyes screwed up concentrated hard. With the picture fixed firmly in her mind Molly Flint always an adventurer made her wish. As if on a bed of feathers very soft feathers Molly floated off.

unit 9
Checking for grammar mistakes

 **Key idea**

To make grammatical sense, verbs must agree with their subjects.

September and October **is** the start of a new year in the tourist industry. ✗

September and October **are** the start of a new year in the tourist industry. ✓

- **Before writing**, try saying sentences in your head or even aloud.
- **While writing**, constant rereading is needed to check that sentences flow.
- **After writing**, rereading the whole text helps the writer to check sense and accuracy.

Try it out! •

⭐ **Top Tip**
Say your sentence in your head before you write it on paper.

Choose the correct form of the verb so that each sentence has grammatical agreement.

(1 mark for each correct answer)

1 The tour guides (is/are) very pleased this year.
2 The weather (is/are) no longer a problem.
3 Last year (was/were) a great success.
4 Customers (was/were) delighted with their holidays.
5 Some travellers (was/were) more adventurous than usual.
6 Nowhere (was/were) too far for them.
7 These travellers (is/are) looking for something different.
8 New places (is/are) harder to think of.
9 A competition (is/are) announced.
10 Top Tourist Rep (is/are) a wonderful title.

Keep practising! ●

Choose a verb and use it in the <u>present tense</u> to make these phrases into sentences. Think about grammatical agreement. An example has been given to help you. *(1 mark for each correct answer)*

Amjit that title. = Amjit wants that title.

Top Holiday Destination

1   She a new advertisement.
2   The advertisement a poster.
3   The poster a beach.
4   Ski slopes behind the beach.
5   A big wheel at the front of the poster.
6   A museum at the back.
7   This poster everything!
8   Amjit her boss.
9   She amazed!
10 The place fantastic.

Take up the challenge! ● ● ● ● ● ● ● ● ● ● ● ● ● ● ● ● ●

Identify and correct the ten grammatical agreement mistakes here.

(1 mark for each correct answer)

Amjit are called to London. She go to head office. She take the poster. Lots of people is waiting. They all looks at Amjit's advertisement. The reaction are marvellous! Amjit are declared the winner. She get her wish: she win the competition. Unfortunately, now she have to find this imaginary place!

· TOP ·
TOURIST
REP

unit 10

Assessment 1

Pronouns 1

A Identify the verb in each sentence. *(0.5 mark for each correct answer)*

1 The spaceship descends at night.
2 It lands on a grassy area.
3 The area happens to be Charley's back garden.
4 They moved into the house last year.
5 Mum expected peace and quiet.

B Identify the tense of these verbs: past, present or future.

(0.5 mark for each correct answer)

1 The spaceship door <u>opens</u>.
2 A small, green creature <u>emerges</u>.
3 The journey <u>was</u> difficult.
4 He <u>had been</u> air-sick most of the way.
5 Earth <u>will be</u> a welcome relief.

Changing tense

Rewrite each sentence in the past tense.

(0.5 mark for each correct answer)

1 Charley stirs under the covers.
2 A light is bothering her.
3 She will get out of bed.
4 She walks over to the window.
5 She will stare in disbelief.

Tenses and text types

Choose the correct label for each text. Either:

narrative: past tense or

explanation: present tense or

forecast/prediction: future tense.

(0.5 mark for each correct answer)

1   There was no time to be frightened – the adventure happened too quickly.
2   Ligaments fasten joints together. Care must be taken that ligaments are not damaged.
3   It will be mild for the next few days, but will turn much colder over the weekend.
4   Diet is important in people's health. Calcium, contained in dairy products, promotes the growth of bones.
5   Every night the princess slept in the same bed. The queen, wanting to test her, placed something beneath the mattress.

Powerful verbs

Which verb is more powerful? *(0.5 mark for each correct answer)*

1   said *or* shouted
2   slammed *or* closed
3   looked *or* stared
4   retorted *or* replied
5   held *or* clenched

Using powerful verbs

Replace the words underlined with one powerful verb. An example has been given to help you. *(0.5 mark for each correct answer)*

A light <u>got in</u> her eyes. A light <u>dazzled</u> her.

1   Charley <u>looked very closely</u> at the garden.
2   She <u>moved</u> her head in disbelief.

3 She <u>held the skin</u> of herself to check she was awake.
4 She <u>took with a quick movement</u> a torch.
5 Charley <u>moved fast</u> down the stairs.

Identifying adverbs

Identify the adverb in each sentence. *(0.5 mark for each correct answer)*

1 The small green man tottered unsteadily.
2 He walked forwards towards Charley.
3 The alien was staring intently at her.
4 He had been told frequently about these creatures.
5 He watched warily as Charley came towards him.

What information adverbs give

Use your answers from the activity above. Give two pieces of information about the five adverbs:
• **the verb qualified by the adverb**
• **the question answered (How? When? Where? or How often?)**
(0.25 mark for each correct answer)

Classifying adverbs

Classify these adverbs in five groups (three words in each), according to meaning. Give a title (for example, "speed") to each classification.
(0.5 mark for each correct group of three words)

sparingly	immediately	finally	distantly	sadly
abundantly	remotely	swiftly	plentifully	willingly
happily	sluggishly	occasionally	closely	hastily

Substituting adverbs

Match the adverb to the phrase that it could replace.
(0.25 mark for each correct answer)

phrases	adverbs
as well as	immediately
for the time being	abruptly
able to be heard	annually
standing out from others	exceptionally
without making an effort	additionally
over the whole country	temporarily
every year	lazily
all of a sudden	nationally
as far as I am concerned	personally
this very minute	audibly

Using commas

Put pairs of commas in these sentences.

(0.5 mark for each correct answer)

1 Charley her heart beating fast kept walking.
2 The torch still held in her right hand made her feel safe.
3 She knew about creatures like this aliens from books.
4 Books even the best ones did not match reality.
5 The pictures as good as they were did not offer this excitement.

Grammatical agreement

Gaps have been left for the verbs. Construct five sentences which make grammatical sense. Make sure the verbs agree with their subjects! *(0.5 mark for each correct answer)*

have/has   offering/offers/offer   befriend/befriends
welcomes/welcome   makes/make   put/puts

1 Charley ... a hand.
2 The green man ... out his claw.
3 They ... a sort of conversation.
4 The alien ... grunting sounds.
5 Charley ... him.

unit 11

Adjectives and adjectival phrases

 Key idea

Phrases, as well as single words, can describe somebody or something.

 Top Tip

Select adjectives and adjectival phrases with care; they should add information to the sentence.

> The **poor** weather lasted throughout January. (adjective)
>
> The weather was **really poor** throughout January. (adjectival phrase)

Adjectives are placed usually before a noun or after a verb.

Adjectives and adjectival phrases are particularly useful in stories and poems.

They can add expression and imagery to writing.

Try it out! ·····················

Identify the adjective and the noun or pronoun described in each sentence.

(0.5 mark for each correct answer)

1 It was a gloomy day at the beginning of February.
2 Through the window, they saw unwelcoming weather.
3 The children decided to stay indoors, out of the drizzly air.
4 With the Professor away, they were alone in the house.
5 The phone's urgent ring unsettled them.
6 An unfamiliar voice greeted Rachel.
7 In a chilly tone, the caller introduced herself as Jane.
8 She had been looking for the house for a long time.
9 She needed to be given detailed directions immediately.
10 Rachel felt nervous whilst she gave the directions.

Rewrite each sentence, replacing the highlighted adjectives with an adjectival phrase from the box. An example is shown below.

(2 marks for each correct answer)

> The *unsettling* phone call worried Rachel and Jack.
> The phone call, *of a disturbing nature*, worried Rachel and Jack.

stretching ahead	absolutely hilarious	impossible to ignore
quite a lot better	not familiar	

1. The **unrecognised** caller had spoken as if she knew the Professor.
2. They told themselves it was probably a mistake and after that, they felt **reassured**.
3. At least the **coming** evening offered some entertainment.
4. They relaxed in front of the **funny** film.
5. Then the doorbell's ring was **insistent**.

Take up the challenge! ●

Fill the gaps with five adjectives and five adjectival phrases.

(1 mark for each correct answer)

The children put the _____ bolt on the door. They settled in front of the _____ film. The _____ bell hurt their ears. The _____ noise came just in the middle of the film. It was the _____ part. Jack got up from the _____ chair. He walked to the _____ door. He remembered the _____ phone call. He also remembered the _____ housekeeper's name. Jane was trying to get into her own _____ house!

unit 12

Comparitive and superlative adjectives

 Key idea

Adjectives can have **comparative** and **superlative** forms.

The comparative form is used when you are comparing two alternatives. (**-er**)

The day had been cold, but the evening was even colder. [comparative]

The **superlative** form compares more than two. (**-est**)

[superlative] It was the coldest day for ten years.

Longer adjectives use **more** and **most** in front of them.

[comparative] A penetrating chill had tuned into a more penetrating frost.
It was the most penetrating frost for twenty years.
[superlative]

Try it out! •

Draw a table like the one below. Write each word in the correct column. An example has been given to help you.

(1 mark for each correct answer)

comparative	superlative
hotter	*hottest*

 Top Tip
Watch out for rare words that disobey the rules. Saying sentences aloud helps.

speedier	wealthiest	hottest	slimmer
funniest	gloomiest	noisiest	mistier
fatter	grander		

Keep practising!

Write the comparatives of these adjectives.
(1 mark for each correct answer)

funny   hot
loud   rainy
quiet   tall
wet   cool
wealthy   late

Take up the challenge!

The adjective in each sentence is in bold. Write its correct comparative or superlative in the gap. In the last sentences, you must choose the correct form. *(1 mark for each correct answer)*

The **loud** music seemed _____ (comparative) than before.

If the sound had been **deafening** then, it was now _____ (comparative).

Chloe, **nervous** before, was now the _____ (superlative) she had been all evening.

Her skin felt **cold,** the _____ (superlative) it had been all winter.

The palms of her hands were **sweaty,** _____ (comparative) than was normal.

She needed a **safe** hiding place, the _____ (superlative) she could find.

A **frightened** Chloe, the _____ she had ever been, spotted her place.

All the cupboards in this room were **big,** but that one was the _____.

The two doors were quite **high,** with one _____ than the other.

Nevertheless, although **short,** Chloe needed to make herself _____.

Adjectives and intensity

 **Key idea**

Adjectives may need to indicate a particular degree of intensity. The correct choice of adjective or accompanying adverb is important.

> The morning was **misty**.
> The afternoon was **greyish**.
> The evening light was **blacker**.
> By 10 o'clock the sky was **quite impenetrable**.

- Adjectives may have similar meanings, but may vary in intensity, for example, "the blackest night".
- An adjective may indicate its degree of intensity by adding a suffix, for example, "a whit**ish** tinge".
- An adjective may indicate its degree of intensity by using an adverb, for example, "**very** funny", "**really** sad".

Try it out! •

Arrange each set of adjectives on an ordered scale. An example has been given to help you.

(1 mark for each set of words in the correct order)

> **size:** tiny ⟶ small ⟶ large

⭐ **Top Tip**
Think carefully about the intensity of meaning of an adjective.

food: delicious tasteless tasty
temperature: warm hot cold
sight: visible invisible panoramic
intelligence: good clever outstanding
condition: spotless filthy marked

wealth: solvent rich poor
health: ill well off-colour
age: old modern antique
mood: angry happy displeased
sound: loud deafening audible

• •

Fill the gaps to produce sets of adjectives on a scale
of intensity. *(1 mark for each set of words)*

1 **light**: dazzling _____ _____ dim
2 **number**: innumerable _____ _____ sparse
3 **distance**: adjacent _____ _____ distant
4 **speed**: supersonic _____ _____ sluggish
5 **size**: mammoth _____ _____ miniature
6 **height**: towering _____ _____ subterranean
7 **happiness**: ecstatic _____ _____ _____
8 **heat**: sizzling _____ _____ _____
9 **mood**: bored _____ _____ _____
10 **handwriting**: copperplate legible _____ _____ _____

Take up the challenge! •

An adverb can be used with an adjective to indicate the adjective's
degree of intensity, for example, "a *fairly* simple idea". Choose
adverbs from the box to fill these gaps appropriately.

(1 mark for each correct answer)

very quite more most really fairly

As Chloe stepped into the _____ enormous cupboard in the
room, she still had to dip her head _____ low. It looked like a
_____ big cupboard from the outside but there was a low shelf
inside it and it was _____ cramped inside. There wasn't much
air in there and it felt _____ suffocating. Once inside the
cupboard, her body seemed an awkward shape, trying to fit into the
_____ impossible space you could think of. As she panicked,
the _____ difficult the task became. Then she took a
_____ deep breath, tried to be _____ patient and thought
in a _____ rational way.

unit 14

Apostrophes to mark contraction

 **Key idea**

An apostrophe may help to make writing sound more natural by shortening words.

> apostrophe of omission   apostrophe of omission

> "I'm fed up," said Rashid. "We've never got anything exciting to do."

- "Contraction" tells you that letters have been left out or omitted. An apostrophe replaces those letters.
- This apostrophe of omission is useful in informal writing and direct speech.

Try it out! •

Match the contraction to its full form. *(1 mark for each correct answer)*

they've	we have
can't	where is
where's	could not
you're	he will
it's	you are
we've	who is
he'll	it is
who's	they have
couldn't	were not
weren't	can not

30

Keep practising!

Make matching pairs of full forms and contractions. You supply the missing halves. *(1 mark for each correct answer)*

1 they are
2 I am
3 he'd
4 who has
5 won't
6 she had
7 hasn't
8 we shall
9 I've
10 shan't

Take up the challenge!

This letter is to a best friend, but it sounds so formal! Replace the words underlined with contractions, using apostrophes of omission.

(1 mark for each correct answer)

Hi Rashid

You are always talking about adventure. Well, I have found it! You can not imagine what has been happening to me. It is all to do with a computer. I had thought about telling other people, but what is the point? They are always laughing at my ideas. I should not tell anyone, but I will let you into the secret ...

unit 15

Apostrophes to mark possession

 **Key idea**

An apostrophe can indicate ownership.

apostrophe of possession

Solomon's discovery was exciting.

The boys' conversation was unusual.

apostrophe of possession

- The apostrophe may be a short way to explain ownership. For example, it is quicker and easier to say "the dog's collar" rather than "the collar belonging to the dog" or "the collar of the dog".
- This apostrophe refers to the owner. In the example above, the owner is "the dog".
- The apostrophe's position varies according to the owner. For example, "the dog's bowl" (the owner is one dog) and "the dogs' bowl" (the owners are two or more dogs).

Try it out! . . . .

 Top Tip
The apostrophe is always placed after the owner's name.

Make the underlined phrase shorter by using an apostrophe. An example has been given below.
(1 mark for each correct answer)

> Rashid and Solomon met *in the house of Rashid*.
> Rashid and Solomon met in *Rashid's house*.

These sentences have singular owners.

1 The note of Solomon had been strange.
2 The writing of the boy had looked peculiar.
3 They did not sound like the usual words of Solomon.
4 Rashid had to discover the secret of Solomon.

5 What was <u>the answer of the question</u>?

These sentences have plural owners.

6 The <u>minds of these boys</u> were always full of adventure.

7 <u>The books belonging to the boys</u> were to blame.

8 <u>The characters in their books</u> had plenty of adventures.

9 <u>The friends of the children</u> were wizards and Martians!

10 What were <u>the powers of wizards</u> in their lives?

Keep practising!

Write an alternative form for these phrases. An example has been given to help you. *(1 mark for each correct answer)*

the dreams of two boys ◆ two boys' dreams

1 tricks by two silly people
2 the judo class for girls
3 a football team for women
4 a sty for a pig
5 the trainers of four children
6 the aerobic class for men
7 the crazy ideas of the children
8 the cage of my pet mouse
9 the houses of Victorian people
10 the taste of the ice cream

Take up the challenge!

Improve the style of the passage by introducing ten apostrophes of possession. *(1 mark for each correct answer)*

The mouth of Rashid hung open. The story of Solomon was finished. The faces of both children were excited, but scared. This was like the mystery of a book! Rashid kept repeating the details of his story. Every computer he touched used the keys of the machine? The fingers of people were not needed? Was the brain of the operator also not necessary? Should they tell anyone else? Should they find out the names of other people? No, this was the adventure of the boys.

Word order

Meaning can be affected by the order of the words in a sentence.

The smallest parcel was in the biggest wardrobe.
The biggest parcel was in the smallest wardrobe.

- It is important to think about what you want to say.
- Your audience needs to understand your meaning.
- Word order can make a difference.

Try it out! •

Put each line of words into an order to make a sentence. *(1 mark for each correct sentence)*

1 a, problem, small, Chloe, had, big
2 fell, Chloe, and, a, moved, shelf
3 Chloe's, hand, the, wood, touched, greasy, broken
4 there, a, crack, loud, was, and, noise, a, splintering
5 space, a, appeared, a, behind, cupboard, the, small, big
6 the, space, open, odd, looked
7 strange, the, place had a, light, eerie
8 Chloe, see, her, could, not, poor, hand
9 this, place, like, was, a, world, weird, different
10 unfamiliar, it, and, was, everything, in, strange

 Top Tip
Make sure that the order you choose for your words makes your message clear.

Use the same line of words as in Try it out! This time change your first order to make a new sentence. *(1 mark for each correct sentence)*

Take up the challenge! •

This text could make better sense. The phrases that are underlined are in the wrong places. Decide where to place them.

(1 mark for each correct sentence)

Chloe was <u>a shimmering, beautiful</u> entering world. It was <u>she was used to</u> completely different from the dreary, dismal winter. <u>Pale blue</u> there <u>like a yellow ball</u> was a sky and a sun. The <u>ordinary human</u> beings she could see were not people. They were <u>as arrows from a bow</u> small and moved as quickly. See them very clearly <u>Chloe could</u>. They took no notice of <u>on the other hand</u> Chloe. But she was not dreaming <u>Chloe pinched herself</u>. She <u>in astonishment</u> gazed open-mouthed.

unit 17

Joining and separating clauses 1

 Key idea

There are different ways to join the parts of a sentence called clauses.

> Solomon wanted to talk to someone **and** he chose Rashid.
> Solomon wanted to talk to someone **so** he chose Rashid.

- A clause is a group of words expressing an event
- A **simple sentence** has only one clause, for example:
  Solomon was excited.
- A **compound sentence** has two or more clauses, for example:
  Solomon had a best friend and he trusted him.

Try it out! ·

Decide whether these sentences are simple or compound. *(1 mark for each correct answer)*

1 Rashid asked Solomon lots of questions.
2 Solomon's face stayed very serious.
3 Solomon was truthful and he was not a practical joker.
4 Rashid was good with computers but this had never happened to him.
5 Solomon's story was exciting but Rashid wanted proof.
6 Then Rashid had a good idea.
7 They could try his computer.
8 It was old but it still worked.
9 The boys went upstairs and Rashid switched the computer on.
10 The computer was old so it took ages to warm up.

> ⭐ **Top Tip**
> Always choose the most effective way of joining clauses together.

36

Make these simple sentences into compound sentences by adding a clause to each one. You must join the clauses with one of these words in the box. *(2 marks for each correct sentence)*

and	but	or	so

Solomon sat down.
He typed some words.
Rashid watched.
Some words appeared.
The boys waited.

Take up the challenge! ●

Put the jigsaw pieces together to make five compound sentences. Write the sentences in the best order to finish the story.

(2 marks for each correct sentence)

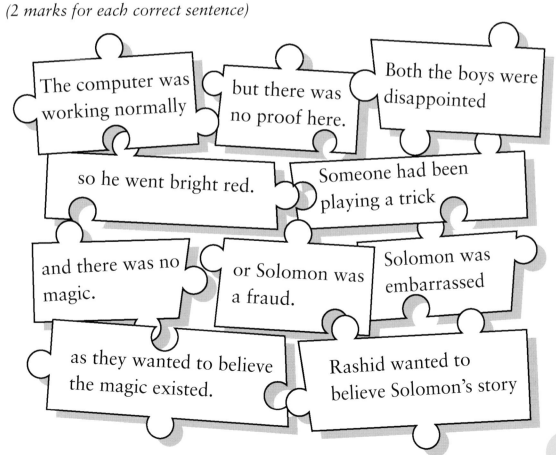

Joining and separating clauses 2

🔑 Key idea

The clauses in a sentence are not always of equal importance.

Although it was busy, Chloe felt alone.

- A complex sentence has a **main clause**.
- Other clauses in the sentence are not as important. They are known as **subordinate clauses**.

Try it out!

Identify the main clause in each sentence.

(1 mark for each correct answer)

⭐ **Top Tip**
Read sentences aloud to find out if commas are needed.

1 There were people, yet they ignored Chloe.
2 The people's clothes were strange, as if they were from a dressing-up box.
3 They reminded her of a picture which was in her history book.
4 When they spoke, they used strange words.
5 Chloe smiled at a boy while he just ignored her.
6 In order to make herself heard, she raised her voice.
7 She pointed to herself, although she felt ridiculous.
8 Although she drew attention to herself, she seemed invisible.
9 Unless there was another explanation, they were ignoring her.
10 While they talked to each other, Chloe listened.

Link two halves to make five complex sentences. Each sentence can have only one main clause. Underline the main clause.

(2 marks for each correct sentence)

while everyone ignored her.
Compared to what Chloe was wearing,
because she looked Chloe's age.
She was very interested in one girl
so that her horrible dress stayed clean.
under which her hair looked terrible.
The girl struggled with a basket
the girl's clothes looked ridiculous!
She was wearing a little white hat,
She wore an apron

Fill the gaps so that the clauses join. Use words like as, if, so that, when, unless, etc. *(1 mark for each correct answer)*

1   The basket looked heavy _____ it was full of vegetables.
2   The girl muttered to herself _____ she walked along.
3   "I must get these peeled _____ Cook needs them."
4   "She will be angry _____ the potatoes are not ready to cook."
5   "They are needed _____ Master and Mistress can have lunch."
6   "_____ I do well, Cook may save me one."
7   "_____ I eat last, I get the leftovers."
8   "I must work hard _____ I can visit mother on Sunday."
9   "I cannot go _____ the Mistress is well."
10   "_____ I have been here a month, it will be my first visit."

Assessment 2

unit 19

Adjectives

Identify the adjective in each sentence and say which noun or pronoun it describes. *(0.5 mark for each correct answer)*

1 It was a fantastic idea!
2 They would have an independent holiday without parents.
3 Harry knew that Gran owned a seaside cottage.
4 She was generous.
5 Certainly, she would let them use her private beach.

Adjectival phrases

Pick out the adjectival phrase in these sentences.

(0.5 mark for each correct answer)

1 The cottage was rather remote.
2 Transport of poor quality served the island.
3 Once you were there, you were almost shipwrecked.
4 The setting was really unusual.
5 The boys were absolutely sure about going there.

Effective adjectives and adjectival phrases

Think about the atmosphere you want to create. Fill the gap with an effective adjective or adjectival phrase. *(0.5 mark for each correct answer)*

1 The cottage was on a _____ island.
2 The island was reached by a _____ ferry.
3 It was a _____ journey across to the island.
4 The weather was _____ when they arrived.
5 Thinking about the time ahead, the boys felt _____.

Comparative and superlative adjectives

Fill in the chart. An example has been done for you.

(0.25 mark for each correct answer)

adjective	comparative	superlative
fierce	*fiercer*	*fiercest*
tall		
wild		
calm		
big		
easy		

Comparative and superlative adjectives

The adjective is underlined. Put its comparative or superlative form in the gap. Remember that not all adjectives use –er and –est. Some need more or most in front of them. *(0.5 mark for each correct answer)*

1 It was <u>late</u> when they arrived but it was _____ when Harry's dad left.
2 There was <u>unpleasant</u> weather everywhere, but this was the _____ part of the country.
3 There was a <u>piercing</u> wind and even _____ rain.
4 If Jamil felt <u>miserable</u>, Harry was _____.
5 After all, Gran was in <u>hot</u> Spain, much _____ than here!

Adjectives and intensity

Arrange these sets of adjectives on scales of intensity. An example has been given for you. *(0.5 mark for each correct answer)*

sparse ⟶ enough ⟶ many ⟶ countless

1 quick slow snail's-pace supersonic
2 miniature huge big small

3   dazzling dim bright clear
4   tall short lofty towering
5   happy sad ecstatic contented

Apostrophes of omission

Put one missing apostrophe in each sentence.

(*0.5 mark for each correct answer*)

1   "Well set up camp on the beach," said Harry.
2   "Oh, Id rather be inside the cottage," argued Dwight.
3   "Itll be more of an adventure out here," replied Harry.
4   "Dont start fighting, you two," shouted Jamil.
5   "I agree with Harry – Ive always wanted to camp."

Apostrophes of possession

Put one missing apostrophe in each sentence.

(*0.5 mark for each correct answer*)

1   The boys previous experience of camping was absolutely nil.
2   This tent was an old one, lent by Harrys father.
3   The tents flysheet was full of holes.
4   The groundsheets waterproofing had long since gone!
5   "Three man tent?" muttered Dwight. "Looks like half a persons tent to me!"

Which apostrophe is which?

Is the apostrophe for omission or possession? You decide. (*0.5 mark for each correct answer*)

1   Three people's hands can be a problem.
2   Jamil's thumb got tied, accidentally, to a peg.
3   "You're doing it on purpose!" he shouted.
4   Somebody else's fingers got caught in the tent ropes.
5   "Now who's laughing?" sneered Jamil at Dwight.

Word order

Re-order the words in each sentence but keep the same meaning. An example has been given for you. *(0.5 mark for each correct answer)*

    At 3 o'clock, they started work on the tent.
    They started work on the tent at 3 o'clock.

1 By 8 o'clock, the tent was finally up.
2 It looked unstable, lopsided, tiny and very unsuitable.
3 As they were starving, the boys no longer cared about the tent.
4 Food, if they could open it, was all they cared about.
5 They only had tins but they had no tin opener.

Joining and separating clauses 1

Make these sentences into compound sentences by adding a clause with one of these words: and   but   or   so
An example has been given. *(0.5 mark for each correct answer)*

    The boys emptied their bags.
    The boys emptied their bags and threw everything on the ground.

1 The boys looked at the food.
2 Jamil had tins of beans.
3 Harry had brought sausages.
4 Dwight started an argument.
5 No one had brought a tin opener.

Joining and separating clauses 2

Underline the main statement in these complex sentences.

(0.5 mark for each correct answer)

1 Although they were famished, the boys were not eating.
2 Tins were useless, unless they could be opened.
3 The boys stared at the tins, as if they could open themselves.
4 Nobody said anything until Harry broke the silence.
5 You two wait here while I phone Mum to rescue us.

Word endings

unit 20

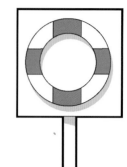

Key idea

Word endings can help identify word classes.

noun

The swimming bath**s** are old.

adjective

My dad jokes that they are even old**er** than he is!

- Certain endings are typical of a word class.
- **–ing** and **–ed** are often at the end of verbs.
- There are plenty of exceptions!

★ Top Tip
Remember that some endings are not much help. Those endings can belong to different word classes.

Try it out!

Write out the word in each sentence that matches the word class shown in brackets. An example has been given to help you. *(1 mark for each correct answer)*

*A brand new water park **was opening**.* (verb)

1 The owners called it Waterworld. (verb)
2 Everyone said it was better than other water parks. (adjective)
3 "Better than the old pools," said Carly. (noun)
4 "Better than the best leisure centres," said Liam. (adjective)
5 "I am waiting to see for myself," said Gran. (verb)
6 It had the highest water chutes anywhere. (adjective)
7 The queues were the longest by miles. (adjective)
8 People waited patiently for two hours to get in. (adverb)
9 The hot sun baked them. (verb)
10 People were expecting good value. (verb)

Copy the chart below. Find ten words from the text to put in the chart. *(1 mark for each correct answer)*

Word endings			
noun: –s, –es	verb: –s, –es, –ed, –ing	adjective: –er, –est	adverb: –ly

Carly, getting near, walked up the path hopefully. Waterworld certainly needed to be good! If she got any hotter, she would melt. Then came the biggest doors she had seen. Palaces were smaller than this! This place looked grander than she was expecting.

Use five of the word endings from Keep practising! Use your words in sentences and state their word classes. An example has been given to help you. *(2 marks for each correct sentence and word class)*

–ly The chute bent sharp*ly* in the middle. (adverb)

Word classes

🔑 Key idea

A word is put into a category or class according to what it does in a sentence (its role).

> verb

Emily and Matt work in a museum. (verb)
The work is very interesting. (noun)

> noun

⭐ Top Tip
Words and their classes may be decided by other words near them in the sentence.

• There are eight main word classes.

• A word can belong to more than one class.

• The word's position in the sentence may affect its role and class.

Try it out! •

Two words are underlined in each sentence: one is a noun and one is a verb. Say which is which. An example has been given to help you.

(1 mark for each correct answer)

The <u>museum</u> in town <u>owns</u> some priceless pottery.

(museum = noun, owns = verb)

1   The relics <u>date</u> from Roman <u>times</u>.
2   They <u>are</u> pieces of Roman <u>pottery</u>.
3   A large, glass case <u>holds</u> the <u>pieces</u>.
4   The <u>curator plans</u> a special day.
5   He <u>wants</u> to open the glass <u>case</u>.

Identify the five adjectives and five nouns. Pair up five sets of adjectives and nouns. An example has been given to help you. *(10 marks)*

adjective	noun
eager	*viewers*
special	knock
exhibition	cramped
reach	accidental
easy	space
museum	small

From the table, use an appropriate word from the correct class to fill each gap. *(1 mark for each correct answer)*

nouns	pronouns	verbs	adverb	prepositions	conjunctions
shriek	it	feels	briefly	until	but
feel		shrieks			
protection		protect			

The museum Open Day is a great success. Crowds come from 9am _____ the late evening. Emily has the job of pottery _____: she must _____ the Roman remains. Her sleepy eyes shut _____. In that moment, a small child takes first a look and then a _____ of a Roman pot. Crash! As the little girl _____ the pot, _____ slips between her fingers. The child _____ in fright, _____ Emily's _____ is even louder. Broken bits are all that remain of the Roman remains!

Commas, semi-colons and colons

 **Key idea**

Different punctuation marks have different functions in a sentence.

> comma   comma   semi-colon
>
> Computer games, if exciting, are very popular; they keep everyone entertained.
>
> colon
>
> Future games may offer more: they may communicate with the player!

- Commas are used to insert additional phrases.
- Semi-colons can link two sentences about the same subject.
- Colons introduce more information.

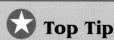 **Try it out!** •••••••••••••••••••••

Extra phrases can be put into these sentences by using pairs of commas. Here is an example. (*2 marks for each correct sentence*)

sentence: A new computer game was created last year.

+ *phrase:* one standing out from others

= A new computer game, one standing out from others, was created last year.

> ⭐ **Top Tip**
> Use punctuation that helps the reader to make sense of your words.

sentences	phrases
Reality Check lived up to its name.	all very realistic
It used unusual situations and interesting characters.	already working flat out
	the new game on the market
Its name soon stirred interest.	appealing and catchy
Customers wanted it.	despite the high price
Manufacturers couldn't produce enough.	

Make five sentences by using semi-colons as a link. Here is an example. *(2 marks for each sentence with correct use of semi-colon)*

The game appeared in June; it was an immediate success.

The game had two main characters.
Deliberately, both were young.
Then you were taken to different levels.
No one thought of anything else.
That was what made it popular.
Reality Check was quicker than other games.
You had to solve puzzles.
Different levels meant more skill.
Those stages had harder puzzles.
Playgrounds filled with *Reality Check* players.

A colon introduces more information. Put the missing colons in these sentences. An example has been given to help you. *(2 marks for each sentence with correct use of colon)*

The manufacturer issued a warning: this game is addictive!

1   Santhos had three hobbies thinking about, planning and playing *Reality Check*.
2   He got up early for one reason he needed to play.
3   It was a competition among these people Santhos, Simoni, Nicos, Dwight and Zoe.
4   One day the rumour started Zoe had moved to level four.
5   Strangely, something else had happened Zoe had disappeared.

unit 23

Dashes, hyphens and speech marks

Key idea

Punctuation marks offer clues to help the reader make sense of a text.

> speech marks   hyphen   speech marks   dash
>
> "You're too soft-hearted," said her nephew – he wanted her to be stricter.

- Speech marks make dialogue stand out.
- A hyphen stresses the connection between two words.
- A dash introduces another thought on the same topic.

Try it out! ●

Two words can join to become one word. Put in ten hyphens. (One sentence needs two.) An example has been given to help you.

(1 mark for each correct answer)

      Emily was spoilt by Great Aunt Matilda.
      Emily was spoilt by Great-Aunt Matilda.

1   Matilda was well off and could afford the best.
2   She owned a five year old cat, called Emily.
3   The best food was served to Emily at dinner time.
4   She was fed from a silver plated dish.
5   She had a special chair in the sitting room.
6   She slept under a silken quilt at night time.
7   The quilt was on her king sized bed!
8   No second hand goods for her!
9   Yet still she was ill tempered.
10 However, she was still well loved.

Keep practising!

Divide Matilda's sentences with a dash. An example has been given to help you. *(1 mark for each correct answer)*

Emily seems unwell – she is off her food.

1 Cook made Emily haddock fish cakes they were her favourite.
2 They were ready at noon Emily liked to eat on time.
3 She ate little maybe she disliked the taste.
4 Cook made her fresh ones she thought cod might be worth a try.
5 She refused them this was so unlike her.
6 Even her milk was not to her taste Cook had left it out a long time.
7 Fearing illness, I tucked her under my quilt her own seemed too thin.
8 The vet was called he knows Emily well.
9 He had a strange expression on his face I hope he understood my concern.
10 "Typical," was what he said I am not sure what he meant.

Take up the challenge!

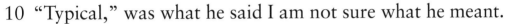

Add these punctuation marks to the passage below:
3 hyphens, 5 dashes, 2 sets of speech marks.
(1 mark for each correct answer)

Are you feeling better, Emily? murmured Matilda. Perhaps you would care for some titbits? Emily accepted the food she had to give in to hunger. The food was served on a gold plated dish Matilda thought she might prefer it. Later the cat set off for a stroll. Most cats are clever this was not the case with Emily. She was empty headed. When the well qualified vet appeared, she forgot to look weak she was out walking. The vet prescribed lots of exercise that would sort her out!

unit 24 Altering sentence type

Key idea

Changing the order of words in a sentence may alter the sentence type.

statement

    Celebrations are taking place.
    Are celebrations taking place?

question

Changing statements into commands (imperatives) is more complicated. For example:
    We will watch what happens. (statement)
    Watch what happens. (command)

⭐ Top Tip
Read the sentence aloud to make sure it makes sense.

Try it out! ·

Identify these sentence types: statement, question or command (imperative). Put a punctuation mark at the end of the sentence. An example has been given to help you. *(1 mark for each correct answer)*
    The streets look different. (statement)

1   What is happening in Lysitania
2   What are the streamers for
3   Listen to what people are saying
4   Read the royal proclamations
5   The great day has arrived at last
6   The Prince is to become King
7   Why is he changing his title
8   What has happened to his father
9   His father has decided to hand over the throne
10 Are people happy or sad

Take note that from this day Prince Parmesan shall be ruler of Lysitania By order of The King

These are statements. Change the word order to make them into questions, as in the example. *(1 mark for each correct answer)*

The King can have a rest. (statement)

Can the King have a rest? (question)

1 He was known as a wise King.
2 He will be remembered for his wisdom.
3 His people have been very happy.
4 They are also happy today.
5 Everyone is celebrating and rejoicing.
6 The Prince will be a popular successor.
7 He is adored by all the people.
8 He will make as good a King as his father.
9 His wife will be a wonderful Queen.
10 Princess Cinderella is loved by everyone.

Change these statements to commands, following the example. Take care with word order and word changes. *(1 mark for each correct answer)*

The palace is repainted. (statement)

Repaint the palace. (command)

1 The streets are swept.
2 Horses are put in place.
3 Trumpets are set ready.
4 Loud fanfares are blown.
5 The Prince and Princess are led out.
6 They are cheered loyally.
7 The royal procession is watched closely.
8 The carriage is guarded.
9 The crowns are brought out.
10 The King and Queen are crowned.

Altering sentence grammar

Key idea

Changing the sentence type may involve more detailed changes.

statement

> The answer to the mystery comes quickly.
> Does the answer to the mystery come quickly? *question*
> Get the answer to the mystery quickly. *command (imperative)*

- Positive statements may add words to make them negative:
  The weather is hot today. (+) The weather is **not** hot today. (–)

- To change into questions, some statements require extra words:
  The temperature will rise. (statement) **When** will the temperature
  rise? (question)

- The focus of a question may depend on its first word:
  Why will the temperature rise?

Verb tense varies in most sentence types, but commands always use
the same verb tense – the present tense.

Try it out! ·

⭐ **Top Tip**
Use as many of the
original sentence's
words as possible.

Make two different questions by using different
wh words in the gap. Use each *wh* word twice.
An example has been given to help you. *(2 marks for each correct answer)*
Why are the seekers on a quest?   *Where* are the seekers on a quest?

1 _____ gave them the idea?
2 _____ could the search be too difficult?
3 _____ are the dangers likely to be?
4 _____ are the seekers likely to meet?
5 _____ will the search end?

Who?   What?
When?
Where? Why?

54

Change these statements from positive to negative. An example has been given to help you. *(1 mark for each correct answer)*

They are meeting at noon. = They are *not* meeting at noon.

1 The seekers are planning to hold a meeting.
2 Their task seems straightforward.
3 Many problems they foresaw have occurred.
4 Success happens very quickly.
5 They need to make faster time.
6 They will have to improve their thinking skills.
7 The group's discussion lasts a long time.
8 People are putting forward different points of view.
9 In the end they reach an agreement.
10 A new leader would be a good idea.

Take up the challenge! ● ● ● ● ● ● ● ● ● ● ● ● ● ●

Put the final punctuation mark at the end of the sentence. Identify the sentence type and verb tense. An example has been given to help you. *(1 mark for each correct answer)*

Days had been wasted. (statement, past tense)

1 What does the leader decide
2 His answer is definite and simple
3 So what is it
4 Think about the clues
5 Use your powers of reasoning
6 The seekers wasted time on red herrings
7 The important clue lay in front of them all the time
8 Remember the clues about noise
9 Why did we bother with hyenas and parakeets
10 Listen to the sounds closer to us

Connectives 1

Key idea

Adverbs and phrases can connect ideas.

> **First,** the gang of friends shared an early breakfast.
>
> **Immediately afterwards,** they set off.
>
> **That is to say,** as soon as Alysha could be dragged away from the table!

- Connectives are helpful linking words. They make the text hang together.
- Adverbs and adverbial phrases can be used as connectives.

Try it out! •

 Top Tip

Reading aloud helps you identify where commas are helpful.

Find the connective (a word or phrase) in each sentence. *(1 mark for each correct answer)*

1 By lunchtime, no one had tried "The Fall".
2 On the one hand, the children were excited at the thought.
3 They were, on the other hand, terrified.
4 Meanwhile the time for going home was getting nearer.
5 As a result, thinking time was running out.
6 However, it seemed impossible to agree.
7 Then Mel became independent.
8 The trip was her idea, after all.
9 She was, besides, the brave one.
10 "Anyway," she said, "I am going!"

Place a comma in each sentence. *(1 mark for each correct answer)*

1   However Mel was still very nervous.
2   More than that she was terrified!
3   Beforehand she had wanted to try this ride.
4   After all the tower could not be that high.
5   Almost immediately she got cold feet.
6   In addition she felt slightly dizzy.
7   All in all she did not feel well.
8   Moreover she wanted to go back.
9   Unfortunately the queue behind her made it impossible.
10 In spite of her nerves she had to keep going.

Take up the challenge! • • • • • • • • • • • • • • • • • • •

Use these connectives to make ten sentences of your own. *(1 mark for*
each correct answer)

within minutes
therefore
finally
suddenly
consequently
nevertheless
some time later
after that
despite that
meantime

Connectives 2

Conjunctions are connectives that join sections of a sentence.

> The park was ideal **because** it had grassy areas.
> **If** the park disappeared, **then** many people would be upset.

- A conjunction joins clauses within a sentence.
- Without the conjunction, the two parts would be separate sentences.
- Some conjunctions work in pairs.

Try it out!

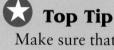

Top Tip

Make sure that the conjunction links clauses.

Identify the connective in each sentence.

(1 mark for each correct answer)

1   Before the supermarket was planned, Sundays were great.
2   Once the gates opened, everyone went to the park.
3   They either played football or they watched the game.
4   When Rio was leaving one Sunday, he saw the notice.
5   It was only a small notice, but it was life-changing.
6   After a month had passed, the park would be built on!
7   The grass would go, so the football pitch would go as well.
8   Although the park was still open, everyone talked about the supermarket.
9   If Rio was going to keep up his football skills, he had to do something.
10 Since no one else did anything, Rio organised a meeting.

What did people say at the meeting? Make up five sentences, using the if … then construction. An example has been given to help you.
(2 marks for each correct sentence)

    If we did not act quickly, *then* it would be too late.

Add a second clause, using one of these connectives to make the join. An example has been given to help you. *(1 mark for each correct answer)*

    Many people came *although* they were not all on Rio's side.

so that	then
yet on the other hand	nevertheless
finally	so
but	that
when	although
once	while
but also	

1   Some people wanted a supermarket …
2   On the one hand people needed to shop …
3   Rio liked food …
4   If the park closed …
5   There was so much arguing …
6   Although there was a lot of noise …
7   Rio made cups of tea …
8   Not only did people shout, …
9   There was quiet …
10 He took charge …

Assessment 3

Word endings

Put the verbs into the past tense by adding the correct word ending: –d or –ed.

(0.5 mark for each correct answer)

1   I arrive at half-past nine.
2   I happen to be the first one there.
3   The other chairs stay empty.
4   I talk to myself for two hours.
5   I realise my dreadful mistake.

Word classes

Identify the adjective and pronoun in each sentence.

(0.5 mark for each correct answer)

1   I am in a big top.
2   It is a hot place to wait.
3   In fact, you could not find a worse place.
4   Eventually, four people join me.
5   They look wonderful athletes.

Commas and semi-colons

A comma introduces a phrase, but a semi-colon replaces a full stop. Choose the correct one for the gap. *(0.5 mark for each correct answer)*

1   We look at each other … eyes wide with curiosity.
2   We all seem similar … we all have the same dream.
3   There is only one place … one space in the team.
4   I have waited for years … this is my first chance.
5   We all feel the same … we all want the job.

Colons

Find a place for a colon in each sentence.

(0.5 mark for each correct answer)

1 The tent flap opens the troupe leader appears.
2 He calls the names Ellie, Alex, Pierre, Asham and Bruno.
3 He says two words "Follow me."
4 A noise startles us the net is going up.
5 We look at each other then we look away.

Hyphens

Two words in each sentence need a hyphen to make them one word. Identify and correct them. *(0.5 mark for each correct answer)*

1 The stand and platform look top heavy to me.
2 Climbers cannot afford to be anything except sure footed.
3 The leader's long fingered hands adjust the ropes.
4 He continues to look stony hearted.
5 He tosses each of us a scribbled and ink smudged note.

Dashes

The troupe leader has left out some punctuation. Put a dash in each sentence. *(0.5 mark for each correct answer)*

1 I climb the ladder I reach the top.
2 The platform sways the ropes feel slippery.
3 The catcher swings towards me I watch in fear.
4 I steady my nerves I leap for the rope.
5 I am swinging through the air it was all worth waiting for.

Speech marks

Correct these sentences: they need speech marks and another punctuation mark. An example has been given to help you.

(0.5 mark for each correct answer)

"I'm going to see the boss," announced Grimbo.

1   We're just not getting the laughs Grimbo told him.
2   What do you think could be going wrong he asked.
3   It's a simple question of timing replied the ringmaster.
4   Your act is just too slow he explained.
5   Can't you think of any quick-fire sketches he said.

Altering sentence type – word order

Change the word order to make these statements into questions. An example has been given to help you. *(0.5 mark for each correct answer)*

Custard pies were becoming ordinary. (statement)
Were custard pies becoming ordinary? (question)

1   People were getting bored with water pistols.
2   Last week's audiences had been small.
3   Their reaction was stony silence.
4   Some people had walked out.
5   The act would need sweeping changes.

Altering sentence type – sentence grammar

Change these statements into questions, adding words and changing word order. Try to include one of the question words. An example has been given to help you. *(0.5 mark for each correct answer)*

We need to make changes.
Why do we need to make changes?

1   The people laugh at things.
2   A sense of humour changes.
3   The audience applauds.
4   They like some things.
5   Some people even cheer.

Identifying sentence type

Identify the verb tense and sentence type. An example has been given to help you. *(0.5 mark for each correct answer)*

Their ideas were not new. (past tense, negative statement)

> sentence types: positive statement negative statement question
> imperative (command)

1 The clowns held numerous meetings.
2 Grimbo's outburst was not encouraging.
3 Listen to me.
4 Did you read the new clown manual?
5 Think like modern people!

Connectives

Make the text hang together by using the connectives in the best places. *(0.5 mark for each correct answer)*

> eventually   almost immediately   in addition
> at the end of a week   but one Monday morning

_____, they were exhausted. _____, they were starting to bicker. _____, they stopped speaking. _____, the boss delivered the latest circus magazine. _____, their spirits were lifted.

Conjunctions

Use a conjunction to join these pairs of sentences.

(0.5 mark for each correct answer)

1 The clowns were tired. They kept working hard.
2 The act was changed. The audience would laugh.
3 Custard pies were out. Buckets of water were still in.
4 They were excited. They were also nervous.
5 The next performance could be a hit. It could be a disaster.

Glossary

adverb
A word that adds meaning to a verb – *The tortoise crawled **slowly**.*

apostrophe (')
A punctuation mark that shows omission of letters when words are contracted (can't; we'll) or possession (Sam's pencil; the dogs' barks)

clause
A group of words that contains a subject and verb – Yesterday it rained. (1 clause); Yesterday it rained and I could not play outside. (2 clauses)

colon (:)
A punctuation mark that separates a word or phrase from additional information about it – The sign read: Keep off the grass.

comparative and superlative adjectives
Used to compare two or more things.
• comparative (two things) – Yesterday was cold, but today is colder.
• superlative (more than two things) – Today is the coldest day for ten years.

connective
A word or phrase used to link parts of sentences or sentences in longer texts – However, he plays both football and rugby.

dash (–)
A punctuation mark that indicates a pause followed by another thought on the same topic – We were surprised – everyone showed up!

hyphen (-)
A punctuation mark that connects two words – cross-country; two-piece

paragraph
A section of a piece of writing, indicated by a new line or indentation.

phrase
Two or more words that act as one unit – the green giant; with a mighty blow

semi colon (;)
A punctuation mark used to link two sentences of equal importance about the same subject: Some people love coffee; others dislike it.